FRANKIE AND JOHNNY

The SAGA OF FRANKIE & JOHNNY

BEAUTIFULLY ENGRAVED BY
JOHN HELD JR

Clarkson N. Potter, Inc./Publisher NEW YORK
DISTRIBUTED BY CROWN PUBLISHERS, INC.

LONG FOREWORD TO A SHORT PREFACE

We in America may have to be satisfied with what might be called a "Lack of Foresight Saga" in *Frankie and Johnny*—"who loved their life away." John Held called it the most famous American saga, and, though it may be short on sweep and grandeur, the raw simplicity and ultimate root-i-toot-toot punch of it obviously appealed to Held, who was marvelously uncomplicated.

In 1930 when this *Frankie and Johnny* was first published, the mood of the country was right to bring out a "sad and tragic story," particularly when the illustrious visual interpreter would "turn your tears of sorrow into peals of laughter." The country was singing Richard Rodgers' "Ten Cents a Dance" and Cole Porter's new hit, "Love For Sale," which was not bad music-to-read-*Frankie-and-Johnny*-by. But Porter's earlier lyrics, "Who could turn my tears to laughter, after you?" might have been even better, and, indeed, Held's *Frankie and Johnny* is much earlier in date than the 1930 "first edition" would indicate.

It was *not* a nostalgic tear-jerking look-back at the Gay Nineties, after the brittle glitter and glamour of the sparkling twenties had shattered into bits and pieces with the crash. On the contrary, Held created the original "linoleum blocks" for *Frankie and Johnny* about 1915, when he was twenty-six years old and living in a seamy rooming house on West 37th Street, which he and fellow talented but impoverished residents fondly called "Cockroach Glades." The Flappers, the Jazz Age, his fame and fortune, were still in the distant and unknown future, whereas the "gay nineties" were still a nearby personal memory.

Most of the men who created our image of New York during the "Jazz Age" were rank outsiders from the West. John Held was born in Utah in the "country of Deseret" in 1889. Thomas Hart Benton was born in Missouri that same year, but Cole Porter would not see the light of day in Peru, Indiana, for another two, and it would be another seven before Scott Fitzgerald would see it in St. Paul. Most of these Americans had a childlike kind of black-and-white approach to "The East"—to the sinful big time. Fitzgerald was compelled to forget his "West" for the "real world," and Porter never stopped running away from Indiana until he died. Benton on the other hand felt morally obliged, ultimately, to reject the big city, after a long love affair with her, but then only with touchingly elaborate reservations.

It was easier for Held. There was no dichotomy, no "either/or" necessity. Nor was it even a delicate balance—Salt Lake and New York were equally valid and happily coexistent components of the cumulative experience of this open and happy man. His easy grace, overpowering good humor, and modesty determined his style. There was no venom, no bitterness, and no very serious purpose. He said once that he presented a certain exhibition "without batting an eye," and this was really always true. Human nature was his subject matter—the position or place made little difference — the fashions and the costumes were only props, only window dressing. No foible escaped him, but he was never cruel in the way he exposed it. He was trenchant yes, mordant, no.

Held was a precocious eleven in 1900, and what he tells us in "A Short Preface" is more fact than fancy. Thus, when these cuts were originally made, they represented a "gay nineties" survival in Held's mind and eye rather than a self-conscious, mimicking revival of a nostalgic style. In a way, then, they are close to being brilliant contemporary satires of Held's still-fresh memories of the excesses of ribald, wood-engraved illustrations in the Police Gazette, which regularly bore captions as outrageous as these in *Frankie and Johnny*. And as such, these cuts are finer works of art than his later efforts in the same vein.

After the birth of the flapper, and the bright lights of *Judge, Life, Vanity Fair*, and the rest of it, the later "woodcuts" done for Ross's *New Yorker* were, perforce, a conscious and sophisticated harking-back to the earlier style. It is known that Held had become familiar with early American and English chapbooks, and their naïveté and directness, undoubtedly, helped him toward his brilliant graphic simplification of the overwrought "engraved style" of the nineties.

These then are Held at his simple, unvarnished, American best. His name has unfairly and inappropriately become synonymous with the "flapper" (which incidentally he just may have invented in an offhanded, unthinking kind of way). All people were funny to John Held, and the shallow, sophisticated flapper would have been good for just one more passing laugh for him, had she not paid off so damn well in good old dollars and cents.

Come to think of it, that must have struck Held pretty funny, too. For in truth he was more of the nineteenth than of the twentieth century at heart, though he could focus his telling and hilarious vision on the immediate world long enough to record and distill it inimitably. So, Ladies and Gentlemen, I give you here true vintage Held, and—cheers!

Carl J. Weinhardt

A SHORT PREFACE

When a youth I learned the song of "Frankie and Johnny" from a colored piano player, who was called "Professor" in a parlor house.

The parlor house was owned and run by a lady who was called Madam Helen Blazes. You may conclude that mine was a misspent youth, but the knowing of these ladies and the houses that they ran has enabled me to fashion this book of wood-cuts from fond memories.

The history and origin of this song has been studied by better minds than mine. Versions in the hundreds have been turned up, but basically the saga is the same. Versions have been evolved to fit the locality, but the story of the eternal triangle remains identical. Details are rearranged to fit geographic conditions. In this illustrated edition, I have taken only the rudimentary verses. I have tried to keep off of local tangents. To many this song will undoubtedly seem incomplete, as verses differ in different parts of the land.

The singers of Frankie and Johnny, who have only the true version are legion, so every man for himself.

The engraving of these blocks has taken many hours and a strong right arm, but in doing them I have lived again a wild free existence in an Inter-Rocky Mountain settlement with my friends the whores, the pimps, the gamblers, the hop-heads and the lenient police, who used to know "The Mormon Kid."

THE SAGA OF FRANKIE AND JOHNNY

with complete illustrative wood-cuts by

John Held, Jr.

1.

Come gather round me, old timers,

Come gather round me, I say,

I'll tell you the story of Frankie and Johnny

Who loved their life away.

For he was her man, and he done her wrong.

I'LL TELL YOU THE STORY OF FRANKIE AND JOHNNIE WHO LOVED THEIR LIFE AWAY

3

2.

Frankie and Johnny were lovers.

Oh, my God, how they loved.

They swore to be true to each other,

True as the stars above,

For he was her man, and he done her wrong.

3.

Frankie worked down in a crib house,

Worked there without any drawers.

FRANKIE WORKED DOWN IN A CRIB-HOUSE

She gave all her money to Johnny

Who spent it on parlor-house whores.

For he was her man, and he done her wrong.

SHE GAVE ALL HER MONEY TO JOHNNY
WHO SPENT IT ON PARLORHOUSE WHORES

4.

Frankie and Johnny were lovers,

Just like every one knows,

Frankie gave her Johnny a hundred dollars

To buy a new suit of clothes.

For he was her man, and he done her wrong.

5

Frankie and Johnny went walking.

Johnny in a brand new suit.

Oh, my Gawd, said Frankie,

Don't my Johnny look cute?

For he was her man, and he done her wrong.

6.

Frankie went up to Ogden.

She went on the morning train.

She gave her Johnny a hundred dollars

To buy a watch and chain.

For he was her man, and he done her wrong.

FRANKIE WENT UP TO OGDEN
SHE WENT ON THE MORNING TRAIN

15

Frankie went down to the corner

To get her a big glass of beer.

She said to the big fat bar-tender,

Has my lovin' Johnny been here?

For he is my man, and he done me wrong.

8.

Then up spoke the big fat bar-tender.

Said, "Frankie, I'll tell you no lie.

Your Johnny was here just a minute ago

With a blonde named Nelly Bly.

If he is your man, well he's doing you wrong."

THEN UP SPOKE THE BIG FAT BARTENDER

9.

Frankie went down to the hock shop.

She bought her a big forty-four;

She aimed a shot at the ceiling,

And shot a hole in the floor.

For he was her man, and he was doin' her wrong.

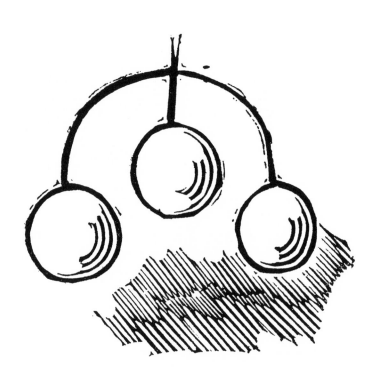

21

10.

Frankie went back to the corner.

This time it wasn't for fun.

Sewed up in her yellow kimono

Was a blue-barrelled forty-four gun.

For he was her man, and he done her wrong.

IN HER YELLOW KIMONA
WAS A BLUE BARRELED FORTY FOUR GUN

11.

Frankie went up to the parlor-house,

She rang on the parlor-house bell.

"Get out of my way, all you pimps and chippies.

Or I'll blow you all to Hell.

For he is my man, and he's doin' me wrong."

STAND BACK ALL YOU PIMPS AND CHIPPIES
OR I'LL BLOW YOU ALL TO HELL—

12.

Frankie went up to the hop-joint,

She looked in a window so high.

There on a bed was her Johnny

Lovin' up Nelly Bly.

But he was her man, tho he'd done her wrong.

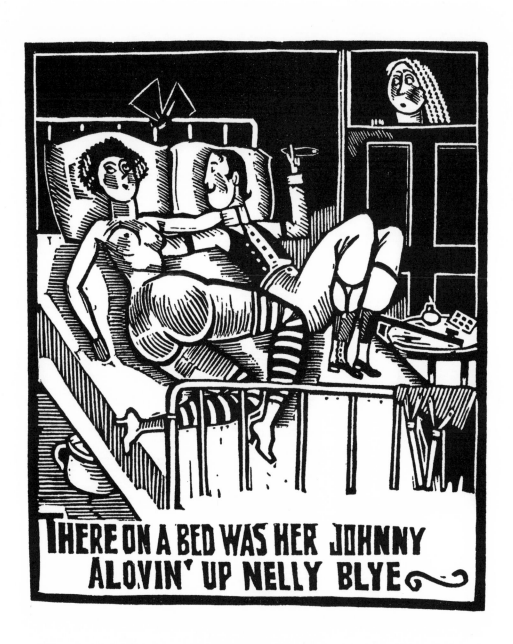

THERE ON A BED WAS HER JOHNNY
ALOVIN' UP NELLY BLYE

27

13.

Johnny ran down the back stairway.

Crying, "Frankie, for God's sake, don't shoot."

But Frankie unlimbered her big forty-four

And the gun went root-i-toot-toot.

For he was her man, and he'd done her wrong.

14.

Turn me over so gently,

Oh, turn me over so slow,

Turn me over to the right side,

So the bullet won't hurt me so.

For I was her man, and I done her wrong.

31

15.

Frankie knelt down at the coffin,

She looked down at Johnny's face.

She said, "God have mercy upon me,

I wish I could take his place.

For he was my man, tho he done me wrong."

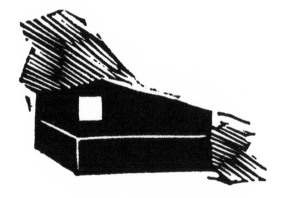

16.

Call out your rubber-tired hearses,

Call out your rubber-tired hacks.

They're taking poor Johnny to the grave-yard

And they aint going to bring him back.

For he was her man, and he done her wrong.

THEY'RE TAKING POOR JOHNNIE TO THE
GRAVEYARD AND AINT GOING TO BRING HIM BACK

17.

Oh, bring on a thousand policemen,

Bring them around today.

Oh, lock me up in a dungeon

And throw the keys away.

For he was my man, and he done me wrong.

LOCK ME IN THAT DUNGEON
AND THROW THE KEY AWAY

37

18.

The sheriff came around in the morning.

Said, "Frankie, it's all for the best."

He said, "Your pimp Johnny

Was nothin' but a God-damned pest.

For he was your man, and he done you wrong."

HE SAID HER LOVER JOHNNIE
WAS NOTHING BUT A GODDAMN PEST

19.

Frankie she said to the warden

What will the verdict be?

And the warden he said to Frankie

It's murder in the third degree.

For you shot your man, cause he done you wrong.

FRANKIE SAID TO THE WARDEN
WHAT WILL THE VERDICT BE ?

20.

I didn't shoot him in the first degree.

I didn't shoot him in the last.

I didn't shoot him in the third degree.

I shot him in the ass.

For he was my man, and he done me wrong.

21.

The judge said to the jury,

"It's plain as plain can be.

This woman shot her lover.

It's murder in the third degree.

For he was her man, and he done her wrong."

THE JUDGE SAID TO THE JURY
ITS PLAIN AS PLAIN CAN BE

22.

Frankie she mounted the scaffold

As calm as a girl can be,

And turning her eyes to Heaven

Said, "Sweet God, I'm coming to Thee.

For he was my man, and he done me wrong."

23.

This story has no moral.

This story has no end.

This story only goes to show

You can't trust no God-damned men.

For he was her man, and he done her wrong.